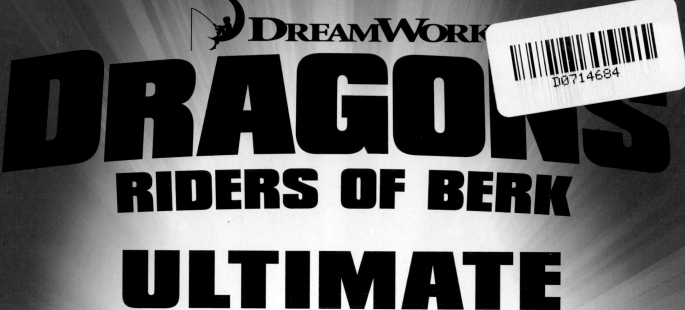

DreamWorks DRAGONS
RIDERS OF BERK
ULTIMATE
STICKER and ACTIVITY

igloobooks

STEALTHY SHADOWS

Toothless is a Night Fury dragon. They are fast and stealthy. Which of these shadowy shapes matches the image of Toothless below?

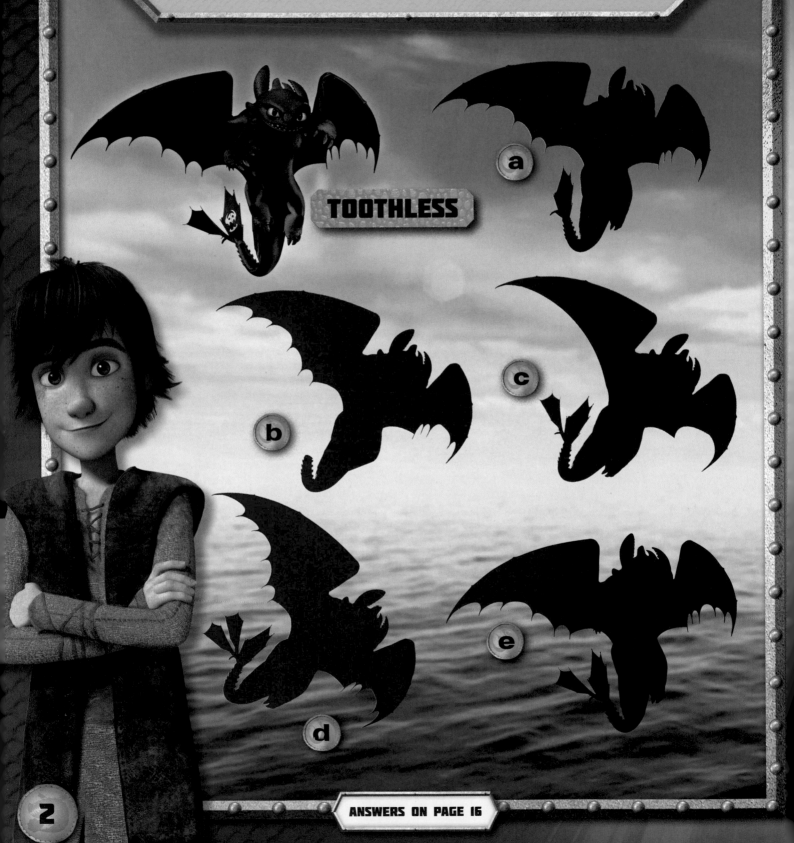

TOOTHLESS

a

b

c

d

e

DRAGON'S LAIR

Help Hiccup to get through the dragon's lair and find Toothless,
but watch out, not all dragons are friendly!

THIS WAY ➞

FINISH

ANSWERS ON PAGE 16

SHIELD SORT

The Dragon Riders all have their own shield with their dragon's crest on. Match the shield to the correct Dragon Rider.

DRAGON SWAP

The Dragon Riders are trying out each other's dragons. Follow the lines to work out who is flying each dragon.

ANSWERS ON PAGE 16

DRAGON DIFFERENCES

Study this picture of the Dragon Riders closely.
Can you spot the eight differences between pictures **a** and **b**?

ENEMY ATTACK

Hiccup needs to work out which dragon is the leader of the enemy pack.
Use the clues below to help him solve the problem.

SEASHOCKER

WHISPERING DEATH

TIMBERJACK

SNAPTRAPPER

CLUES

1. The leader doesn't have a brown body.
2. The leader has more than one head.
3. The leader has a green body.

ANSWER

Snaptraper

DRAW A DRAGON

What would your ideal dragon look like?
Use the space below to draw it.

FRIEND OR FOE?

An enemy dragon has tried to sneak into the Dragon Rider's camp.
Circle the dragon that does not belong to any of the Dragon Riders.

MORE THINGS TO FIND

1 Boat
 2 Sheep
3 Jugs
 4 Shields
5 Baskets
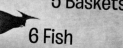 6 Fish

AWESOME
IN ACTION

ULTIMATE
RIDER

IN DRAGONS
WE TRUST

TEAM
TOOTHLESS

TEAM
STORMFLY

TEAM
MEATLUG

TEAM BARF
AND BELCH

TEAM
HOOKFANG

FLIGHT PATH PROBLEMS

The Dragon Riders are racing high above Berk. Who has the fewest obstacles in their way and will get to Berk Island first?

HICCUP

FISHLEGS

RUFFNUT & TUFFNUT

BERK ISLAND

ANSWERS ON PAGE 16

DRAGON RIDER RACE

1. Place your coins on the start space and take turns to roll the dice. The player with the highest roll goes first.
2. Roll the dice and move that number of spaces clockwise around the board, following the special instructions when you land on an action square.
3. Each time you land on an emblem square, find the matching sticker on your sticker sheet and place it in the correct space on your sticker grid.
4. Continue around the board until you have collected all the emblems. Then, it's a race to the finish space. The first player to get there wins!

START

1

2

3 Catch a lift on a dragon! Go forward 4 spaces.

4

28

FINISH

21 Tame a wild dragon! Roll again.

20

27

22

26 A dragon poops on you! Go back to the start.

25

24

23

8
Stoick stops
you! Miss a
turn.

9

7

10

6

11

5

12
Your dragon is
fastest! Choose
a player to move
back 2 spaces.

13

19

14

18

17
Mildew shouts
at you! Go back
3 spaces.

16

15

How well can you draw?
Copy this picture of Toothless square by square into the grid below.

CLOSE-UP TROUBLE

Look at this image of the Dragon Riders closely. Three of the close-up images below are not part of the larger scene, can you find them?

a

b

c

d

e

f

ANSWERS ON PAGE 16

ROUND 'EM UP

The sheep have escaped. Without going diagonally or in the same square twice, find a route that passes over all the sheep and gets you to the finish.

START

FINISH

ANSWERS ON PAGE 16

DRAGON TAKEDOWN

Enemies are attacking Berk. Close your eyes and use your finger to target enemy dragons. Every time you correctly hit a target, give yourself a point.

PLAY AGAINST A FRIEND
The first person to hit all five dragons wins.

ANSWERS

PAGE 2: STEALTHY SHADOWS

e is the correct shadow.

PAGE 3: DRAGON'S LAIR

PAGE 4: SHIELD SORT

a-4, b-5, c-1, d-2, e-3

PAGE 4: DRAGON SWAP

a-3, b-4, c-1, d-2

PAGE 5: DRAGON DIFFERENCES

PAGE 6: ENEMY ATTACK

The leader of the enemy
dragons is Snaptrapper.

PAGE 8: FRIEND OR FOE?

PAGE 9: FLIGHT PATH PROBLEMS

Fishlegs will get to Berk first.

PAGE 13: CLOSE-UP TROUBLE

Pictures a, c, and e are not part of
the scene.

PAGE 14: ROUND 'EM UP

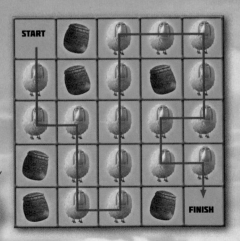

DREAMWORKS
DRAGONS
RIDERS OF BERK
COPY COLOURING FUN

HOW TO USE THIS SECTION:

1. Read about the dragons and Dragon Riders.

2. Place the right sticker for each character on each page.

3. Copy-colour the stickers of Hiccup, the rest of the Dragon Riders and their dragons.

4. If the picture has a dragon emblem, find it on your sticker sheet and add it to your Emblom Collection on page 32.

Collect all 6 emblems to get the 7th and become a Dragon Master.

HICCUP

Hiccup is the leader of the Dragon Riders. He works hard to make sure there is friendship and trust between dragons and Vikings.

ASTRID

Astrid is Hiccup's friend. Her strength and bravery are always called upon when the Dragon Riders are on an adventure.

TOOTHLESS

Toothless is a Night Fury dragon, the rarest of all the dragons. His rider is Hiccup and together they protect the skies over Berk.

STORMFLY

Stormfly is a Deadly Nadder dragon, a perfect mix of beauty and strength. Her rider is Astrid and together they are a powerful team.

Use your best pens to decorate this scene of
the Dragon Riders and their dragons.

SNOTLOUT

Snotlout can be stubborn,
but when Berk is in danger,
he will do anything
to protect it.

EXTRA STICKERS

SNOTLOUT

HICCUP

RUFFNUT AND TUFFNUT

FISHLEGS

ASTRID

TOOTHLESS

STORMFLY

MEATLUG

BARF AND BELCH

HOOKFANG

AWESOME
IN ACTION

READY TO
FLY?

ULTIMATE
RIDER

IN DRAGONS
WE TRUST

TEAM
TOOTHLESS

TEAM
STORMFLY

TEAM
MEATLUG

TEAM BARF
AND BELCH

TEAM
HOOKFANG

BERK TRAINING ACADEMY

FISHLEGS

Fishlegs knows a lot about dragons. He has studied hard and can identify nearly every different type of dragon.

HOOKFANG

Hookfang is a Monstrous Nightmare dragon. These dragons are known to be fierce and strong. They can also set themselves on fire for defence in an attack.

MEATLUG

Meatlug is a Gronckle dragon. Though quite slow and sleepy, Gronckle dragons are the toughest species of dragon in the world.

RUFFNUT AND TUFFNUT

This brother and sister team are constantly messing about and fighting with each other, but when danger is near, they team up to protect their friends and Berk.

BARF AND BELCH

Barf and Belch make up a Hideous Zippleback dragon. Having two heads can be a challenge, but when both heads work together, they can create explosive firepower.

Together the Dragon Riders become a team that has everything they need to succeed - strength, wisdom, friendship and awesome dragons!

EMBLEM COLLECTION

Use this page to collect your emblem stickers.
You are only 6 stickers away from becoming a Dragon Master.

Congratulations!
You are now a Dragon Master.

NAME: Hiccup
DRAGON: Toothless
STORY: Hiccup is the leader of the Dragon Riders. He is brave, smart and caring. He loves his dragon, Toothless, very much and will do anything to protect him.

NAME: Astrid
DRAGON: Stormfly
STORY: Astrid is one of the bravest people on the team. Astrid's not afraid to jump into an adventure and use her fierce fighting skills.

NAME: Snotlout
DRAGON: Hookfang
STORY: Snotlout is a bit of a bully, and not very clever, but is a skilled warrior. He likes to show-off and thinks he's as good a Dragon Rider as Hiccup.

NAME: Ruffnut & Tuffnut
DRAGON: Barf & Belch
STORY: Ruffnut and Tuffnut are twins who love to compete and fight with each other which sometimes gets them into trouble.

NAME: Fishlegs
DRAGON: Meatlug
STORY: Fishlegs knows a lot about dragons. Whenever the team needs to know about an enemy dragon, Fishlegs always has the answer.

THE RIDERS OF BERK

The island of Berk is where Hiccup and the rest of the team spend most of their time. Use your sticker sheets to add all the Dragon Riders to this fun picture.

MISCHIEF MAKERS

In Berk, the dragons are causing trouble. The villagers have had enough of their mischief. Use your sticker sheets to add lots of destructive dragons causing chaos.

"Let go of my food!
Drop it, pesky dragon!"

NAME: Toothless
DRAGON TYPE: Night Fury
STORY: Toothless is a Night Fury dragon. He is the only one of his kind known to exist. Night Fury dragons are amazingly fast flyers and can shoot bright purple plasma blasts and fly at super-sonic speeds.

NAME: Stormfly
DRAGON TYPE: Deadly Nadder
STORY: Stormfly is a Deadly Nadder dragon. She is a fire-breathing dragon and has sharp spines on her tail that she can shoot with deadly accuracy.

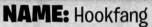

NAME: Hookfang
DRAGON TYPE: Monstrous Nightmare
STORY: Hookfang is a strong and hot-tempered dragon. Hookfang can cover his body in flammable gel and set himself on fire to defend against enemies.

NAME: Barf & Belch
DRAGON TYPE: Hideous Zippleback
STORY: Barf and Belch are a two-headed dragon. One head breathes gas that creates a green, smelly fog and the other head emits a spark which lights up the gas and creates a powerful and incredibly hot flame.

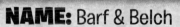

NAME: Meatlug
DRAGON TYPE: Gronckle
STORY: Meatlug is a large and loyal dragon who likes to sleep. His fire-breathing skills are different from the other dragons. He eats rocks and turns them into red-hot balls of lava, then fires them at his enemies.

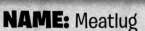

DRAGON BIOGRAPHY

VILLAGE VILLAINS

Hiccup is trying to tame the dragons and stop them from causing trouble in the village. Find as many stickers as you can and make the village as messy as possible!

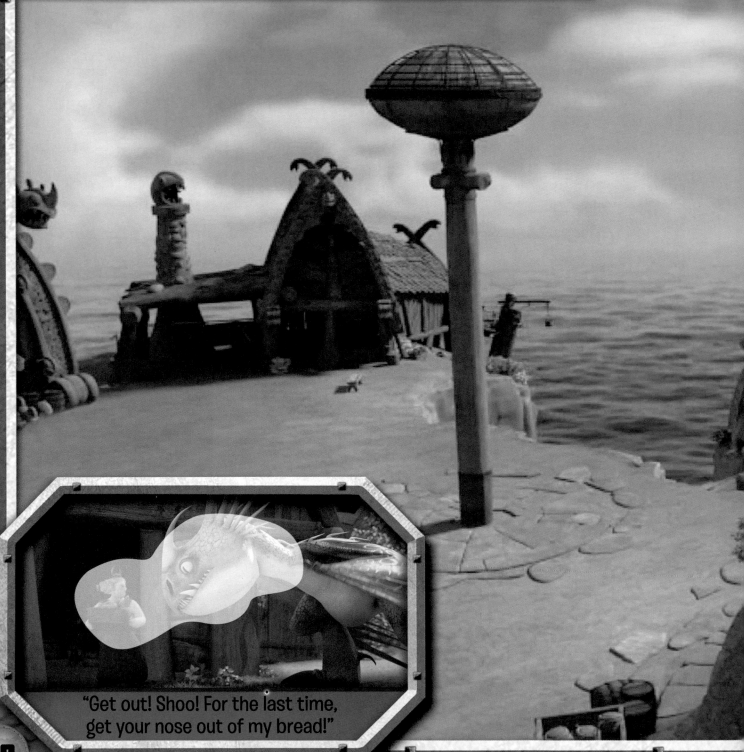

"Get out! Shoo! For the last time, get your nose out of my bread!"

Page 34

Page 35

Page 36-37

Page 38

Page 38

Page 39

Page 40

"You need to put those dragons in cages, Stoick."

"Hiccup! What's going on out there? The plaza looks like a war zone," says Stoick. "Don't worry, I have a plan," replies Hiccup.

"All right, we've got a lot of training to do, but together, we can keep these dragons under control."

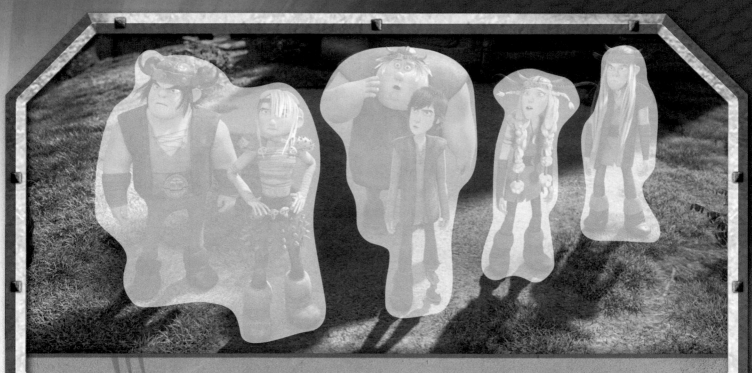

Later that day, after training, Hiccup, Astrid and the other Dragon Riders go to the village, but there's a problem.

"How can I trust you to control all the dragons, when you couldn't even control your own?" says Stoick. "Oh, Toothless, what have you done?" says Hiccup, frustrated.

BACK TO THE CAGES

Stoick has told Hiccup and his friends that the dragons need to be locked away because of the mess they are making. Use your stickers to add all of the dragons to the scene.

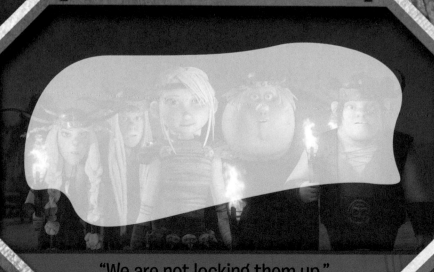

"We are not locking them up."

"Look, the dragons are gonna do what they're gonna do. It's their nature. We just need to learn how to use it to help us."

A HELPING HAND

Hiccup decides to train the dragons to help the villagers.
Add some cool stickers to this scene to show the
dragons helping the fishermen.

"Snotlout, you and Hookfang can
scare us up some dinner!"

"You just saved us three months of work. I'm proud of you, Hiccup," says Stoick. "This Dragon Training Academy is for you! Now all you have to do is train them!"

"Dragons can't change who they are. But who would want them to? They are strong, powerful creatures and I am going to learn everything there is to know about dragons. Wouldn't you?"

TRAINING ACADEMY

Hiccup and the rest of the Dragon Riders now have their very own
Dragon Training Academy! Use your sticker sheets to
add Hiccup, Toothless and all their friends.